Contents

- UNIT 1 Music and Me 4
- UNIT 2 Let's Move! 6
- UNIT 3 My Shoes 8
- UNIT 4 Music Box 10
- UNIT 5 Spoon Orchestra 12
- UNIT 6 Cock-a-Doodle-Doo 14
- UNIT 7 Good for You 16
- UNIT 8 Green Light, Go! 18
- My Progress 20
- Cutouts C1
- Stickers S1

The Bebop Friends

UNIT 1: Music and Me

Lesson 1

🎧 Count the school objects. Listen to the pieces of music. Point to the side of the table with a few or many school objects on it according to the music.

Unit 3   Stickers

 Listen and play bingo.

UNIT 2 — Let's Move!

Lesson 1

 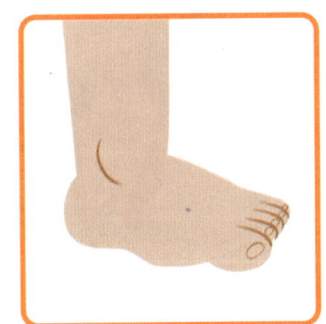 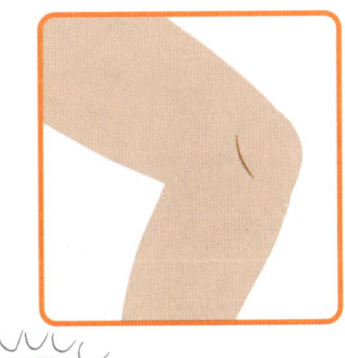

 Connect the movements with the body parts. Listen and move your body.

 Listen, point, and say. Sing the song: *Run Run!* Listen and do the actions.

UNIT 3 — My Shoes

Lesson 1

S1 Stick the correct clothes on Leopold and Clementine. Sing the song: *Hot and Cold*. Point and say the clothes in the pictures. Listen and mime Leopold or Clementine according to the tones.

Lesson 2

 Connect the characters to their shoes. Sing the song: *Boots and Ballet Shoes*. Walk like a giant and a ballet dancer. Listen to the song again and play along with your shoes.

UNIT 3

9

UNIT 4 Music Box

Lesson 1

🎧 Point and say. Count the balloons. Color the white balloons pink. Find and circle the gift box.
Sing the song: *Happy Birthday!*

Lesson 2

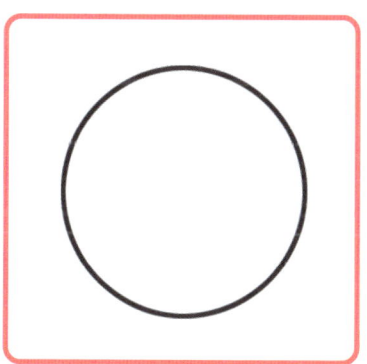   

 Listen and play. Point and say the toys. Connect the toys to the correct picture. Color the toys. Circle your favorite toy.

UNIT 5 — Spoon Orchestra

Lesson 1

🎧 Listen to the song: *High and Low*. **C1** Take Ruth upstairs or downstairs according to the sounds. Listen and move your finger to the purple or red side of the piano keyboard according to the chords.

Unit 5   Cutout

Unit 8   Cutout

Lesson 2

 Point to the objects and imitate their sounds. Circle the objects that produce short sounds with black. Circle the objects that produce long sounds with pink. Listen, play along, and dance.

UNIT 5

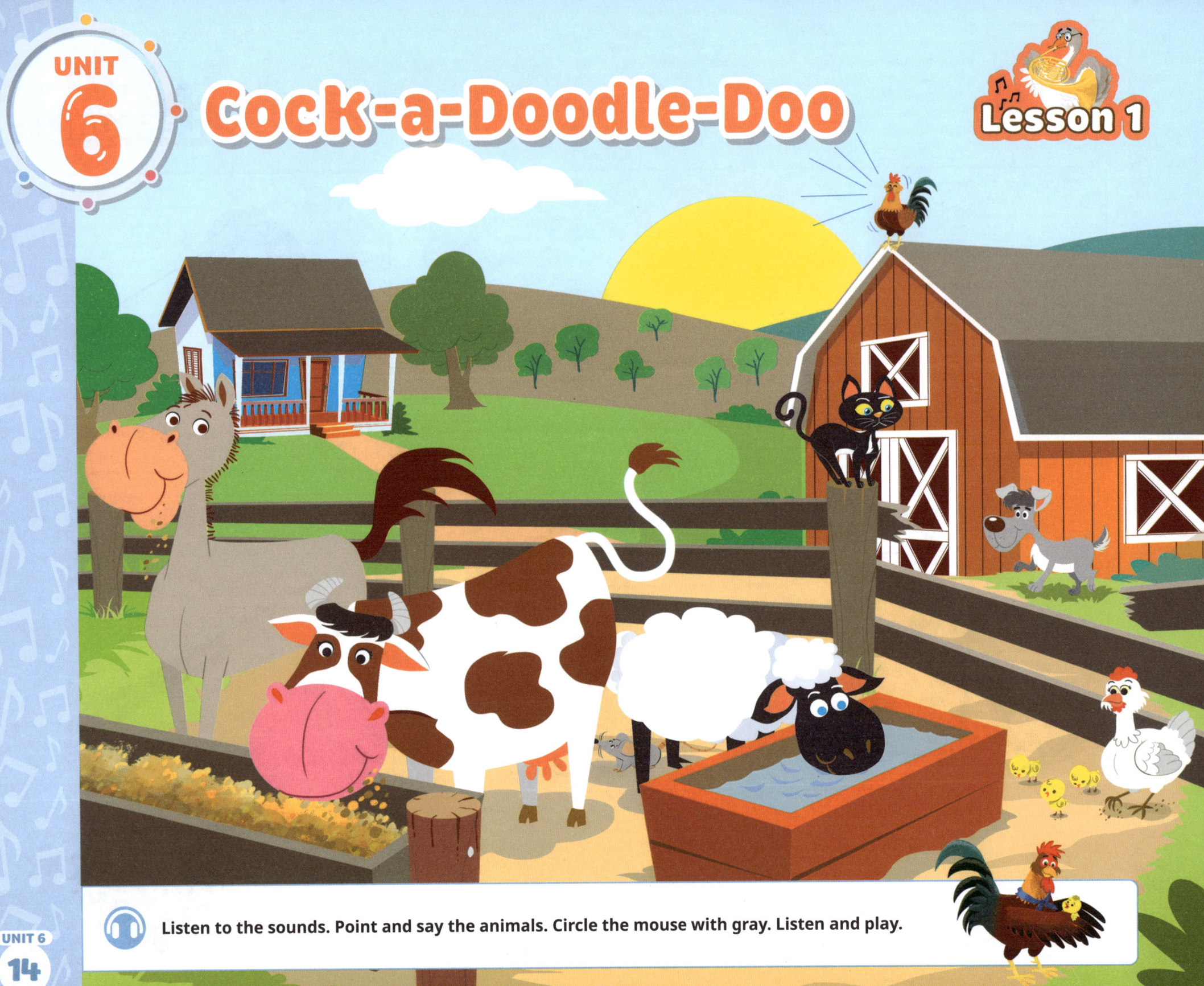

Lesson 2

 Connect the instruments and their places in the picture. Sing the song: *The Farm Animal Band* and dance.

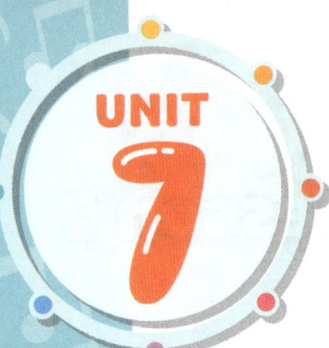

UNIT 7

Good for You

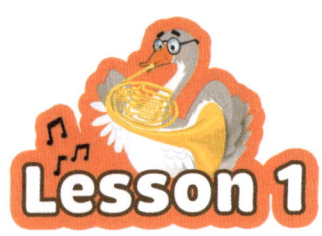

Lesson 1

1

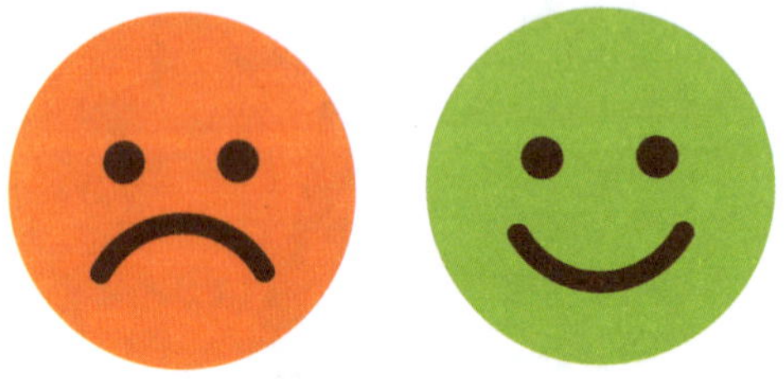

2

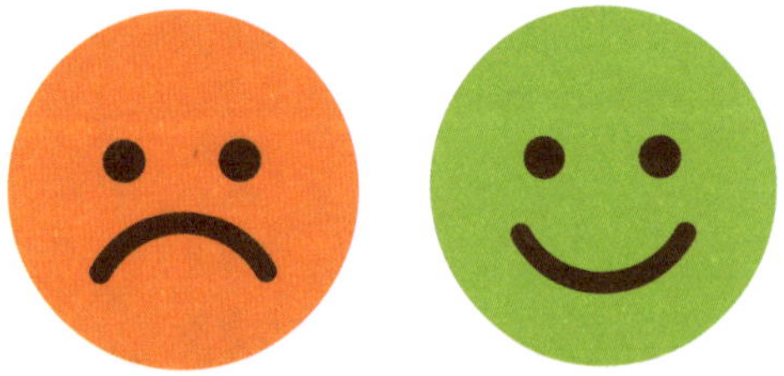

3

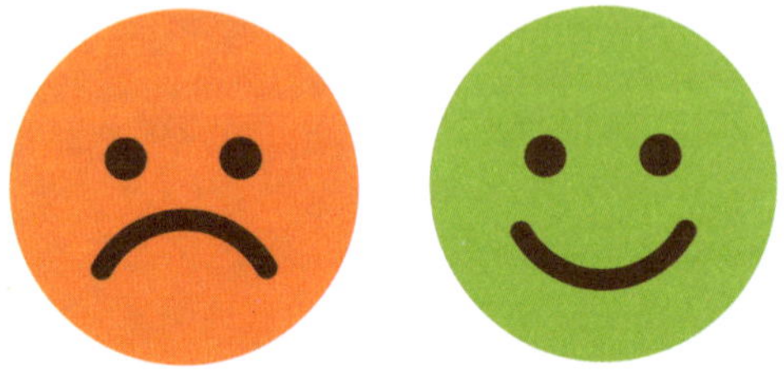

4

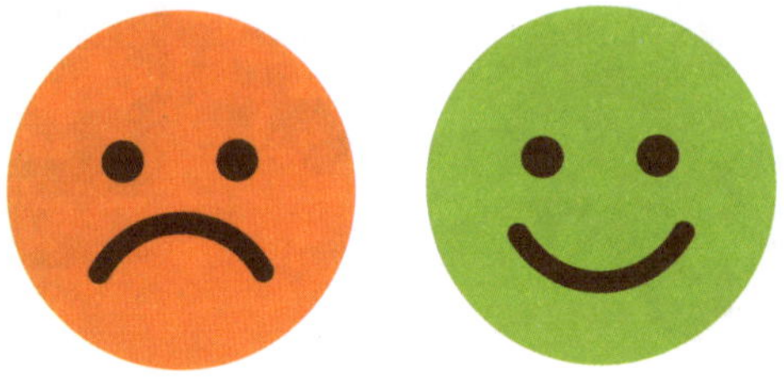

5

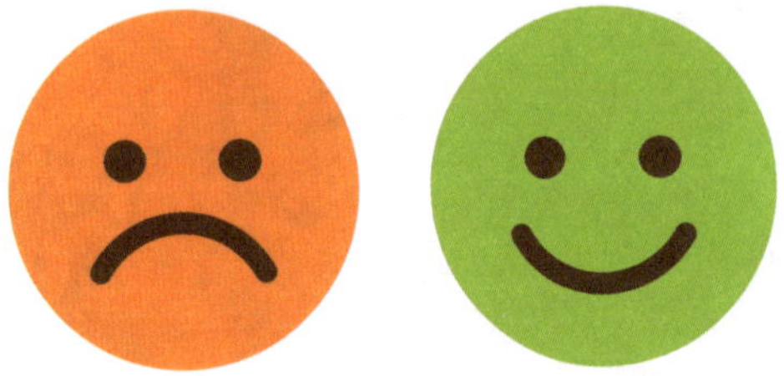

6

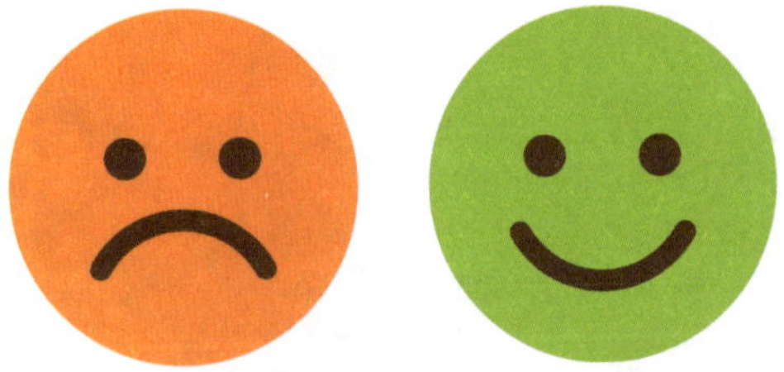

Listen, circle, and say *I like it. / I don't like it.*

Lesson 2

 Point and say the food. Sing the song: *Good and Bad for You*. Connect the food to the correct circle. Sing, walk, and act out good and bad.

UNIT 8 Green Light, Go!

Lesson 1

Point and say the places in town. Sing the song: *Let's Go to the Park!* Clap as you sing feeling the steady beat. C1 Help Paul and his mommy cutout cross the streets.

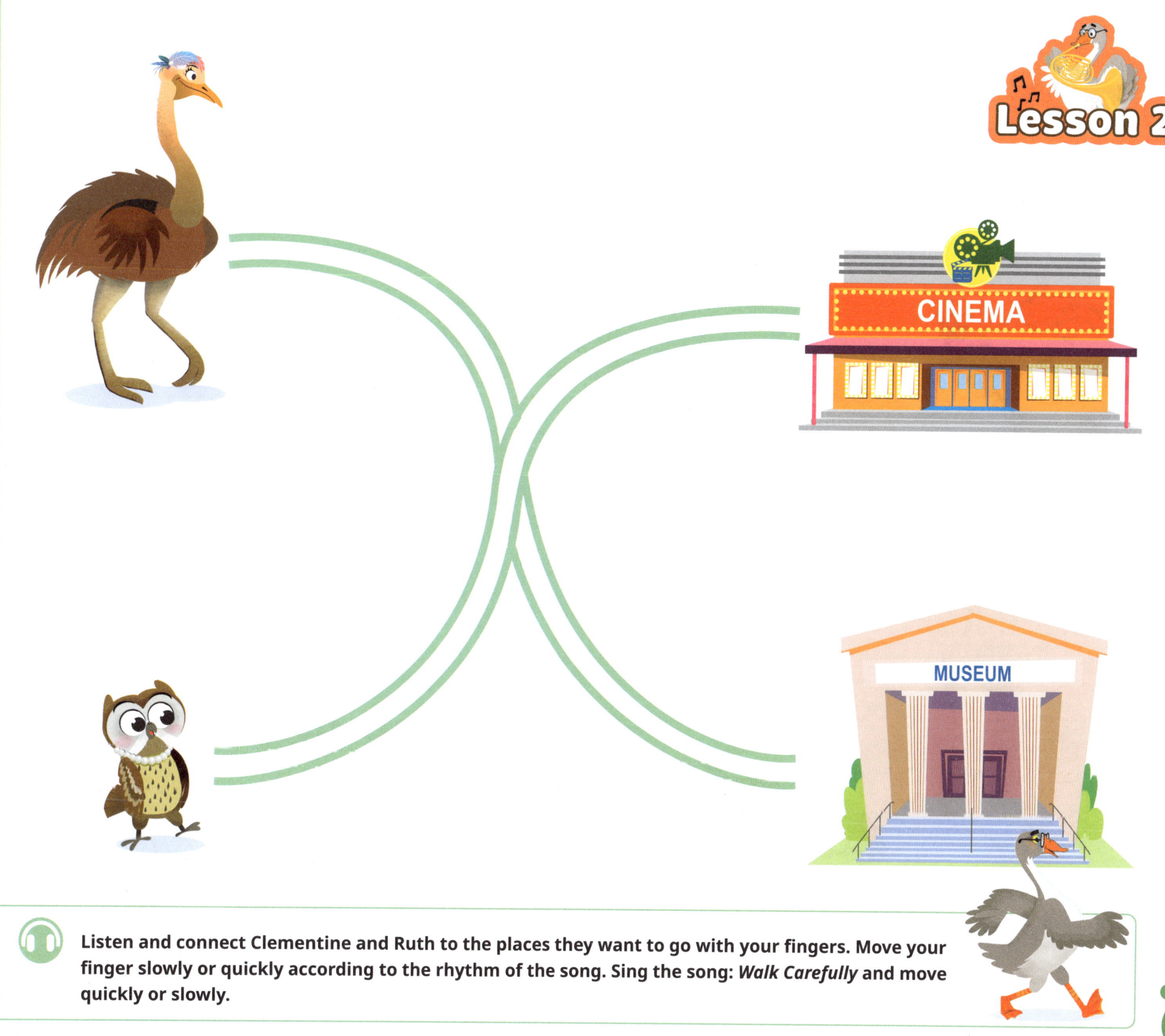

Lesson 2

Listen and connect Clementine and Ruth to the places they want to go with your fingers. Move your finger slowly or quickly according to the rhythm of the song. Sing the song: *Walk Carefully* and move quickly or slowly.

My Progress

Color the number after you complete the unit.

Macmillan Education Limited
4 Crinan Street
London N1 9XW

Companies and representatives throughout the world

Bebop and Friends Level 2 Music Book ISBN 978-1-035-10944-9
Bebop and Friends Level 2 Music Book with Music eBook Pack ISBN 978-1-035-10945-6

Text, design, and illustration © Macmillan Education Limited 2022
Written by Claudia Mol and Cláudia Mariza de Carvalho

The authors have asserted their rights to be identified as the authors of this work in accordance with the Copyright, Designs and Patents Act 1988.

This edition published 2022
First edition entitled "Bebop" published 2014 by Macmillan Education Limited

All rights reserved. No part of this publication may be reproduced, stored in a retrieval system, transmitted in any form, or by any means, electronic, mechanical, photocopying, recording, or otherwise, without the prior written permission of the publishers.

Design by Macmillan Education Ltd, with contributions by Design Divertido
Page makeup by Figurattiva Editorial
Illustrated by Ilustra Cartoon, Michelle Todd (The Bright Agency) p. 2
Cover design by Macmillan Education Limited

The publishers would like to thank Rich Rafterman, Argila, and Minke Edição e Produção Cultural.

The authors and publishers would like to thank the following for permission to reproduce their photographs:

Getty Images/iStockphoto/Thomas Lydell p. 5, Getty Images/iStockphoto/PeterHermesFurian p. 5, Getty Images/iStockphoto/Vectorpower p.5, Getty Images/iStockphoto/aekikuis p. 5, Getty Images/iStockphoto/Jiripravda p. 5, Getty Images/iStockphoto/TheArtist p. 5, Getty Images/iStockphoto/Ekaterina Bedoeva p. 5, Getty Images/iStockphoto/JohnGollop p. 13, Getty Images/iStockphoto/EHStock, p. 13, Getty Images/iStockphoto/Photobalance p. 13, Getty Images/iStockphoto/Bet_Noire p. 13, Getty Images/iStockphoto/xxmmxx p. 13, Getty Images/iStockphoto/bortonia p. 16, Getty Images/iStockphoto/Magone p. 17, Getty Images/iStockphoto/atiatiati p. 17, Getty Images/iStockphoto/hdere p. 17, Getty Images/iStockphoto/aiaikawa p. 17, Getty Images/iStockphoto/Tim UR p. 17, Getty Images/iStockphoto/Liudmila Chernetska p. 17

These materials may contain links for third party websites. We have no control over, and are not responsible for, the contents of such third party websites. Please use care when accessing them.

The inclusion of any specific companies, commercial products, trade names or otherwise does not constitute or imply its endorsement or recommendation by Macmillan Education Limited.

Printed and bound in Uruguay

2022
1